The Good

MENOPAUSE
DIET COOKBOOK

Healthy Eating Feel-Active Plan & Symptom Management For Menopausal Women

THE GOOD FOOD MENOPAUSE DIET COOKBOOK
HEALTHY EATING FEEL-ACTIVE PLAN & SYMPTOM MANAGEMENT FOR MENOPAUSAL WOMEN

ISBN: 9781913005443

DISCLAIMER

CONTENTS

MAIN MEALS

SNACKS, SWEET TREATS AND SIDE DISHES

INTRODUCTION

Now is the time to embrace a common sense approach to food. Instead of being concerned with food fads and foibles, mid-life is an opportunity to seize control of your dietary habits in order to gain increased health and a long and energetic life.

Approaching middle age is a time of great change for most of us. We may have children who are getting older and more independent, we may be entering a new stage in a relationship, embarking on a career change or looking towards an early retirement. The number of changes that may occur are as varied and individual as we are as women.

However, there is one change that is largely universal and a rite of passage for the majority of women: the menopause. In fact, it is so defining that it is often simply referred to by its colloquial nickname: 'The Change'.

WHAT IS MENOPAUSE?

In simple terms, the menopause is when a woman stops having periods and is no longer able to become pregnant through natural means. Contrary to popular belief, this is not the time when your period stops, but rather twelve months after your last period. This is a protracted process and periods usually start to become less frequent over a few months or years before they stop altogether. Women often experience other side effects alongside this, many of which can be irritating and uncomfortable.

The average age for a woman to reach the menopause is 51, but around 1 in 100 women experience the menopause prematurely, before 40 years of age.

The experience is different for each individual, but largely follows the same broad strokes. For most women, the experience begins when they reach their forties, and their bodies begin to enter the perimenopause stage. This is the period before menopause, where oestrogen and progesterone levels drop and fertility decreases. During this stage, women may find that they experience a variety of side effects which may include: missed periods, PMS, breakthrough bleeding, palpitations, migraines, hot flushes, vaginal dryness, insomnia and anxiety.
After this, women reach menopause. Some women may be lucky enough to experience few side effects, but for many, it's a time when the reduction in oestrogen levels can result in hair loss, aches and pains, fatigue and weight gain. Even if you manage to escape the worst side effects of changing hormone levels, many women are left with a general feeling of sluggishness or malaise.

BENEFITS OF AGING

All of this may make for depressing reading, but it is important to bear in mind that this is a natural part of life that also brings with it many advantages. Many women feel relieved to escape the monthly tyranny of periods, and the ability to not worry about unwanted pregnancy leads many to embrace a new and improved stage of their sexual lives.

Menopause comes at a time for many women when they can embrace their own individual needs, often occurring shortly after a time when life may have been spent caring for others' needs before their own. Mid-life can bring about a new-found appreciation for the important things in life and leads many to re-evaluate their future plans. In some ways, it's like beginning a New Year and for some women it holds the opportunity to make the ultimate New Year's resolution: a new phase in life brings new commitments to self-improvement.

As with a New Year's resolution, many people look towards improving their health. The symptoms described above, combined with general aging and a search for more energy, lead many women to evaluate their diets. There are many hundreds of options available. It often seems that every month there's a new diet promising us the world, with pseudo-science, unrealistic time or financial commitments, or simply unappetizing recipes on offer. That's where one of, if not the, most wonderful aspects of getting older comes in: life wisdom and experience. It is this that shows us that faddy diets, weird and wonderful concoctions, expensive meal plans or diet clubs are all unlikely to give us any of the benefits we crave in the long-term.

A COMMON SENSE APPROACH

Now is the time to embrace a common sense approach, based on years of experience. Instead of being concerned with food fads and foibles, mid-life is an opportunity to seize control of your dietary habits in order to gain increased health and a long and energetic life.

Many women have complex relationships with food, often seeing it as an enemy to be resisted, and feel like they spend their life in a battle against cravings, desires and weight gain. As a result, enjoying food is often seen as a negative thing: gluttonous, naughty and often leaving one plagued with guilt after taking pleasure from a meal or snack.

Middle-age is the perfect time to break away from this damaging mindset. Instead of seeing food as an enemy, it should be embraced as an ally; helping you to achieve your health goals, manage menopausal symptoms and give you the energy needed to enjoy the next stage in your life.

After all, the link between diet and energy is direct: food is fuel. The most beneficial way to eat, if you wish to alleviate the symptoms of middle-age, is to ensure you have a balanced diet that nourishes your body, heart and soul.

WHAT TO EAT AND ENJOY

Food is something to be enjoyed, and that is why, in this book, you will find that taste comes first in every recipe. This is underpinned by well-established nutritional common sense - no fads or cod science! These are not 'clean-eating' or super food, detox or calorie-counted recipes. Instead, you will find food that contributes to a balanced and diverse diet, with less sugar, better fat and good carbs; a diet which is full of fresh vegetables and 'good' carbohydrates (which release their energy slowly throughout the day leaving you satisfied for longer), together with some dairy and lean protein.

Sometimes, symptoms of menopause and low energy levels can be brought about by a deficiency in nutrients, particularly the essential B vitamins, which help convert our food into fuel, enabling us to stay energised throughout the day. Mineral deficiencies - such as iron levels being low - can leave you feeling tired and off-colour, and a lack of potassium can also result in a drop off from peak performance.

To combat these issues, you'll find these recipes full of B vitamins from chicken, nuts, leafy greens and eggs, iron in the form of an occasional serving of lean red meat, and potassium from bananas: all of which will leave you bursting with vim and vigour.

Alongside what we need to eat for our health, our lifestyle is important too. Food isn't something that should have us chained slavishly to the stove when there's so much of life for us to see and embrace! As such, these recipes are created with realistic lifestyles in mind: quick mid-week dinners, lunches that can be made as quickly as a sandwich and travel well, and family-favourites for multi-generational weekend meals - all of which can be made with easily available ingredients that won't break the bank.

By embracing your future, and throwing away long-held and damaging attitudes towards food, you will be able to enjoy eating delicious food from these recipes, as well as enabling yourself to counter the symptoms of menopause. Each recipe contains a chef's note explaining how each recipe will aid and sustain your health, leaving you able to look forward to the next stage in your life as a woman, minus any guilt and stress, and full of health and energy.

BREAKFAST

TURMERIC LATTE

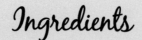

Ingredients

- 200ml/7floz full fat coconut milk
- 200ml/7floz unsweetened almond milk
- 1 tsp honey
- 1 tbsp ground turmeric
- 1 tsp ground cinnamon

- 1 tsp ground ginger
- 1 tbsp coconut oil
- 1 tbsp chia seeds
- 3-4 ice cubes

Method

1 Combine all the ingredients except for the chia seeds into a saucepan and warm everything gently until just before it reaches boiling point. It should smell aromatic and fragrant.

2 Pour into a mug or heat-proof glass.

3 Sprinkle chia seeds on top and enjoy straight away.

CHEF'S NOTE

Turmeric has numerous health benefits that will help alleviate menopausal symptoms. It's anti-inflammatory, blood sugar-stabilising and can help to regulate the body.

STRAWBERRY SMOOTHIE

Ingredients

- 200g/7oz coconut milk
- 120ml/4floz frozen or fresh strawberries
- ¼ tsp vanilla extract
- ½ tbsp lemon juice

Method

1 Place all the ingredients in a blender and mix until smooth.

2 Taste, and add more lemon juice if desired.

3 Pour into a tall glass and serve immediately.

CHEF'S NOTE

Strawberries contain five of the B-complex vitamins, as well as vitamins K and E: all crucial nutrients that help control hormone levels, which may be out of balance pre, during and post-menopause.

CHOCOLATE NUT GRANOLA

Ingredients

- 250g/9oz cashews, roughly chopped
- 250g/9oz hazelnuts, roughly chopped
- 150g/5oz cocoa powder
- 125g/4oz pecans, roughly chopped
- 125g/4oz ground flaxseed
- ½ tsp cinnamon

- ½ tsp ground nutmeg
- 60ml/2floz coconut oil, melted
- 60ml/2floz maple syrup
- 1 tsp pure vanilla extract
- 60g/2½oz dark chocolate chips

Method

1 Preheat the oven to 150C/300F/gas 2. Line a rimmed baking sheet with parchment paper.

2 Combine the cashews, hazelnuts, cocoa powder, pecans, flaxseed, cinnamon and nutmeg in a large mixing bowl. Mix until all ingredients are well combined.

3 In a separate small bowl, combine the coconut oil, syrup, and vanilla extract. Mix until all ingredients are well incorporated.

4 Pour the coconut oil mixture over the dry ingredients and toss to coat until all ingredients are evenly mixed and coated.

5 Spread the mixture in a single layer across the prepared baking sheet.

6 Bake for 60 minutes, tossing every 15 minutes.

7 Remove from the oven and allow to cool. The granola will continue to crisp as it cools.

8 When cold stir through the chocolate chips.

CHEF'S NOTE

This homemade granola is full of slow-release carbohydrates and has a high fibre content which should help you feel fuller for longer, maintaining steady energy levels to power you through the morning.

PUMPKIN SPICE GRANOLA

Ingredients

- 250g/9oz pecans, roughly chopped
- 150g/5oz walnuts, roughly chopped
- 150g/5oz almonds, roughly chopped
- 150g/5oz ground almonds
- 60g/2½oz flax seeds
- 60g/2½oz pumpkin seeds
- 60g/2½oz sunflower seeds
- 60g/2½oz melted butter
- 1 tsp honey
- 1 tsp cinnamon
- 1 tsp vanilla
- ½ tsp nutmeg
- ½ tsp salt
- 60ml/2floz water

Method

1 Preheat oven to 130C/ 250F/ Gas ½.

2 In a large bowl, combine all the ingredients. Mix very well.

3 Place a piece of parchment paper on a baking tray and grease it. Spread the granola on the tray. Place a second piece of parchment on the granola.

4 With a rolling pin, roll the granola, to compress it into a firm and even sheet. Remove the top piece of parchment and discard.

5 Bake for about 60 to 90 minutes, or until golden, throughout. Remove from the oven and allow to fully cool before breaking into pieces.

CHEF'S NOTE
Nuts and seeds like the pumpkin, sunflower and almonds in this recipe contain vitamin E, zinc and calcium. These vitamins, and the oils in nuts and seeds, may help prevent dry skin which is common in middle age.

15

FRUITY CEREAL BARS

Ingredients

- 125g/4oz cup raw pecans
- 125g/4oz raw almonds
- 10 Medjool dates, pitted
- 125g/4oz apple, grated
- 125g/4oz almond butter

- 125g/4oz coconut flakes
- ½ tsp ground cinnamon
- ½ tsp vanilla extract

Method

1 Pulse the pecans and almonds in a food processor until they reach a flour-like consistency then place them in a large bowl.

2 Process the dates in the food processor until they turn into a soft paste.

3 Add the date paste to the nuts and combine with all the remaining ingredients, stirring until everything is well combined.

4 Divide the mixture into tablespoon-sized portions and squeeze together to form a small bar shape.

5 Refrigerate for an hour or two and then serve.

CHEF'S NOTE
Apples and dates are both high in boron, this is a mineral which is important for the regeneration of bone and helps to reduce the risk of developing osteoporosis.

SMOKED SALMON AND SCRAMBLED EGGS

Ingredients

- ½ tsp butter
- 2 medium eggs, beaten

- 25g/1oz smoked salmon, roughly chopped

Method

1 Heat the butter in a small saucepan over a medium-low temperature.

2 Season the eggs with black pepper and stir in the salmon. Pour into the saucepan.

3 Cook very gently for 3–4 minutes, stirring slowly, until the eggs are scrambled. Remove from the heat and stir for a few seconds.

4 Spoon onto a warm plate and serve.

CHEF'S NOTE

Both salmon and eggs are high in omega-3s; eating them twice a week as part of your menopause diet may help reduce inflammation, a possible contributor to heart disease.

BREAKFAST BAKE

Ingredients

- 8 eggs
- 2 green bell peppers, deseeded and finely sliced
- 80g/3oz chestnut mushrooms, halved and thinly sliced

- 40g/1½oz spinach, roughly chopped
- 50g/1¾oz mature cheddar cheese, grated

Method

1 Preheat the oven to 180C/160C Fan/Gas 4.

2 Lightly grease a 35cm/14 in x 25cm/10in 2cm/¾in deep roasting tin and line with baking paper.

3 Crack the eggs into a large bowl, add the salt and pepper and whisk well.

4 Pour the eggs into the oven tray making sure they spread into the corners. Scatter the peppers, mushrooms and spinach over the eggs and top with the cheddar.

5 Place in the oven to bake for 10–12 minutes, or until just set and lightly golden around the edges.

6 Remove the tray from the oven and leave to rest for 2 minutes, then slide out onto a board and cut into pieces.

CHEF'S NOTE

A good breakfast is always the best start to the day, but it becomes even more important during menopause; it ensures your blood sugar levels are regulated, helping to prevent middle-aged spread.

GREEN EGGS AND HAM

Ingredients

- 1 handful kale, chopped with the stems removed
- 200g/7oz frozen spinach, thawed and squeezed dry
- 6 large eggs
- 2 tbsp milk

- 25g/1oz Parmesan cheese, grated
- 25g/1oz mild feta cheese, crumbled
- 25g/1oz ricotta cheese
- 1 tbsp parsley or chives
- 2 slices of ham, chopped

Method

1 Finely chop the kale and spinach.

2 Add the eggs, milk and Parmesan and mix until well combined.

3 Mix the feta, ricotta and chopped fresh herbs in another bowl and season with pepper. Set aside.

4 Heat 1tsp of olive oil in a non-stick pan and pour in half of the egg mixture. Fry on a medium heat until just set.

5 Add half the feta and ricotta mixture, and half of the ham on top and gently fold the omelette over. Place a lid on the pan and cook for another minute until the filling is warmed.

6 Grate some extra Parmesan on top and keep warm whilst you make the second omelette.

CHEF'S NOTE

Not just for Dr Seuss fans! Kale contains a substance that boosts your liver's ability to metabolise oestrogen; this increases collagen production which naturally declines during menopause.

NORTH-AFRICAN EGGS

Ingredients

- 1 tbsp olive oil
- 1 large onion, chopped
- 1 red and 1 green bell pepper, cut into long slices
- 1 clove of garlic, crushed
- ½ tsp cumin powder
- ½ tsp cayenne pepper
- 1 tbsp tomato purée
- 4 salad tomatoes, chopped
- 4 eggs

To serve:
- 4 tbsp Greek yoghurt

Method

1 Heat the olive oil in a large, lidded frying pan. Add the onions, peppers and garlic then season with salt and pepper. Cook on a medium heat until soft. Add in the cumin and the cayenne pepper.

2 Stir in the tomato purée and cook for a couple more minutes before adding the tomatoes with a splash of water.

3 Simmer for 10 minutes or so, uncovered, until reduced a little and the tomatoes are soft. If it becomes too thick (it should have a pasta sauce consistency) then add a touch more water.

4 Make 4 small wells in the sauce and break an egg into each. Place the lid on the pan and cook for roughly 4 minutes or until the whites are just set and the yolks are still runny.

5 Serve with the yoghurt drizzled on the top.

CHEF'S NOTE
This dish makes a fantastic weekend brunch that feels special and easily scales up. If you do not suffer from hot flushes, then consider adding some chopped chilli (this may trigger those who are susceptible).

SERVES 2

MUSHROOM OMELETTE

Ingredients

- 1 tbsp olive oil
- 250g/9oz sliced chestnut mushrooms
- 1 crushed garlic clove

- 1 tbsp thinly sliced fresh chives
- 4 large beaten eggs

Method

1 Heat the oil in a small frying pan over a high heat. Stir-fry the mushrooms in three batches for 2-3 mins, or until softened. Tip the cooked mushrooms into a sieve and drain the excess cooking juice.

2 Return all the mushrooms to the pan and stir in the garlic and chives with a pinch of ground black pepper. Cook for a further minute, then reduce the heat to low.

3 Preheat the grill to its hottest setting. Pour the eggs over the mushrooms. Cook for five mins, or until almost set.

4 Place the pan under the grill for 3-4 mins until set. Serve immediately or allow to cool.

CHEF'S NOTE
Mushrooms and eggs are both high in protein and make a quick, filling meal at any time of the day. Olive oil is a "good fat", which promotes healthy joints.

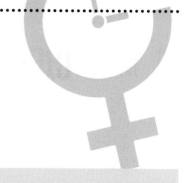

BAKED AVOCADOS

Ingredients

- 1 avocado
- 2 eggs
- Salt and pepper

- 2 slices of linseed bread
- 2 tsp flat-leaf parsley, chopped

Method

1 Preheat the oven to 180C/350F/gas mark 4. Cut the avocado in half, remove the stone and scoop a little extra of the flesh out.

2 Break the first egg into a bowl. Using a spoon, place the yolk in one half of the avocado, then carefully start to add the white (you may not manage to add it all). Season with salt and pepper, then repeat with the other egg and half of an avocado.

3 Place the avocado halves in a small baking dish that fits them snugly and bake for 15-20 minutes, or until the white is opaque and the yolk is done to your liking.

4 Toast the bread and serve with the avocado and, seasoned with salt and pepper and scattered with the parsley.

CHEF'S NOTE

Linseed contains phytoestrogens, which help to balance hormones and are thought to prevent hot flushes and other menopausal symptoms.

MEXICAN EGGS

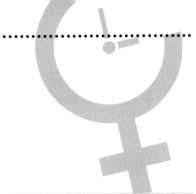

Ingredients

- 4 tbsp coconut oil
- 4 garlic cloves, minced
- 1 orange bell pepper, chopped
- 1 white onion, chopped
- 2 jalapeños, finely diced

- 2 tomatoes, diced
- 4 eggs
- A bunch of coriander/cilantro
- 1 avocado

Method

1 Heat half of the coconut oil in a frying pan over medium heat.

2 Fry the garlic, pepper, onion and jalapeños for 3 minutes, or until the onion is translucent and the peppers have softened slightly.

3 Add the diced tomatoes and cook for 5 minutes before setting aside.

4 Place a separate nonstick pan over medium-low heat and add remaining coconut oil.

5 Slow-cook the eggs for approximately 6 mins or until the whites cook through.

6 Plate the eggs topped with the vegetable mix, and garnish with coriander and avocado slices.

CHEF'S NOTE
Eggs are among the most nutritionally balanced foods, a fantastic source of protein and sustained energy to help beat fatigue.

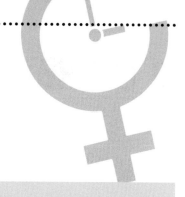

VANILLA OATS

Ingredients

- 50g/2oz jumbo porridge oats
- 200ml/7floz soya milk
- ½ tsp vanilla extract
- 2 tbsp natural yoghurt
- 25g/1oz chia seeds

Method

1 Mix all the ingredients in a bowl and leave to soak for at least 20 mins.

2 If the porridge is too dry after this time, then add a little water.

3 Divide the mixture between 2 bowls and top each with blueberries, flaked almonds and honey or any other combination of fruit and nuts you would prefer.

CHEF'S NOTE
Soya is high in phytoestrogens which could potentially help with hot flushes, one of the most common menopausal symptoms. Try increasing your intake of soya milk, tofu and edamame to feel the benefits.

BIRCHER MUESLI

Ingredients

- 50g/1¾oz porridge oats
- 2 coarsely grated apples
- 20g/¾oz roughly blanched hazelnuts, roughly chopped
- ¼ tsp ground cinnamon
- ¼ tsp ground nutmeg
- 200g/7oz Greek yoghurt
- 100ml/3½floz skimmed milk
- 100g/3½oz blueberries
- 10g/¼oz toasted flaked almonds

Method

1 In a bowl mix the oats, apples, hazelnuts, cinnamon and nutmeg.

2 Stir in the yoghurt and milk and cover the bowl before leaving the mixture to chill in the fridge for several hours or overnight.

3 When ready to serve spoon into two bowls and top with the blueberries and almonds.

CHEF'S NOTE

Oats contain the amino acid tryptophan which helps manufacture the neurotransmitter serotonin. Serotonin helps moods and may help control sleep and appetite.

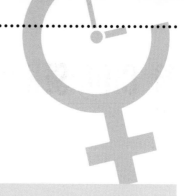

BANANA PORRIDGE

Ingredients

- 2 small bananas, halved lengthways
- 100g jumbo porridge oats
- ¼ tsp cinnamon

- 150ml milk of your choice, plus extra to serve
- 4 walnuts, roughly chopped

Method

1 Preheat the oven to 190C/375F/gas 5. Mash up one banana half, then mix it with the oats, cinnamon, milk, 300ml water and a pinch of salt, and pour into a baking dish.

2 Top with the remaining banana halves and scatter over the walnuts.

3 Bake for 20-25 mins until the oats are creamy and have absorbed most of the liquid.

CHEF'S NOTE

Bananas are bursting with potassium; this is why many distance runners rely on bananas to fuel them through a race as potassium is an essential element for energy.

CHIA SEED PUDDING

Ingredients

- 175ml/6floz coconut milk
- 2 tbsp chia seeds

- ½ tsp vanilla extract

Method

1 Mix all the ingredients in a non-metallic bowl or jar.

2 Cover, place in the fridge and leave overnight.

3 Serve the pudding with yoghurt, coconut milk or some fresh or frozen berries.

CHEF'S NOTE

Chia seeds are a good source of omega-3 fatty acids; these help raise HDL cholesterol, the "good" cholesterol that protects against heart attack and stroke.

BREAKFAST PANCAKES

Ingredients

- 2 eggs
- 250ml/ 8½floz milk
- 1 tsp vanilla extract
- 200g/7oz wholemeal flour

- 1½ tsp baking powder
- 1 tsp ground cinnamon
- Spray oil

Method

1 Whisk the eggs, milk and vanilla together in a jug.

2 Sieve the flour into a mixing bowl and add the baking powder and cinnamon. Gradually add the wet ingredients to the dry and whisk together. Add a pinch of salt and leave to rest for 1 hour.

3 Heat a spray of oil in a frying pan on a medium heat. Add a large spoonful of batter to the pan to make a pancake.

4 Once golden, flip the pancake over. Repeat with the remaining batter until it's all used up. In between pancakes separate them with baking paper and keep warm in a low oven.

5 To serve put the pancakes on plates, and top to your taste with fruit, yoghurt, cream or shaved dark chocolate.

CHEF'S NOTE

Swapping white flours for wholemeal is a simple swap that can help ensure health throughout middle-age and beyond.

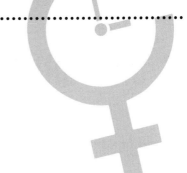

RASPBERRY MUFFINS

Ingredients

- 125g/4oz blanched almond flour
- Pinch of baking soda
- Pinch of salt
- 2 tbsp honey
- 120ml/4floz coconut milk
- 2 tbsp melted coconut oil
- 1 egg
- 60g/2½ oz fresh or frozen raspberries

Method

1 Preheat the oven to 190C/350F/gas mark 5 and line a muffin tin with paper cases or use a non-stick silicone muffin pan.

2 Mix together the almond flour, baking soda and salt.

3 In a separate bowl, whisk together the honey, coconut milk, coconut oil, and egg.

4 Mix the wet and dry ingredients together until just combined but be careful not to over mix.

5 Gently fold in the raspberries into the batter.

6 Spoon batter into the prepared muffin tin, filling each to the top.

7 Bake for around 20-25 mins, until a skewer inserted into the centre comes out clean.

8 Wait until muffins are completely cool before serving.

CHEF'S NOTE

Experimenting with different types of flours is a fantastic way to reduce your levels of carbohydrates. These muffins are tastier than shop-brought, and won't result in a mid-morning sugar crash.

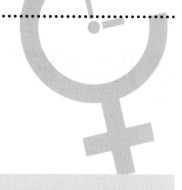

SAVOURY EGGY-BREAD

Ingredients

- 2 large eggs
- 2 slices of whole-wheat bread
- 1 tsp tomato purée

- ½ tsp Worcestershire sauce
- 1 tsp olive oil
- 2 tomatoes, each cut into four thick slices

Method

1 Crack the eggs into a wide, shallow bowl and whisk with a fork.

2 Spread one side of each slice of bread with the tomato purée and sprinkle over the Worcestershire sauce.

3 Place the bread slices into the egg mixture and soak for 5 minutes, turning three times.

4 Heat the oil in a frying pan over a medium heat. Fry the tomatoes and egg-soaked bread for 3–4 minutes, turning halfway through, or until lightly browned on both sides.

5 Serve immediately.

CHEF'S NOTE

Tomatoes contain large amounts of vitamin B-6, which help maintain ideal oestrogen-progesterone balance. It is when these hormones are unbalanced that menopause symptoms can be difficult to control.

RICOTTA POTS

Ingredients

- 200g/7oz ricotta
- A pinch of ground cinnamon
- 2 tsp runny honey
- 200g/7oz blueberries

Method

1 Mix the ricotta with the cinnamon and half of the honey in a bowl.

2 Gently stir in most of the blueberries. Divide the mixture between two ramekins or small bowls.

3 Top with the remaining blueberries and keep in the fridge, covered, until ready to eat.

4 Drizzle over the remaining honey just before serving.

CHEF'S NOTE
Ricotta is incredibly versatile and high in calcium and vitamin D. Both are important in preventing bone density loss, which occurs after the menopausal drop in oestrogen.

OATY BREAKFAST BOWL

Ingredients

- 50g/2oz jumbo gluten free porridge oats
- 200ml/7floz unsweetened almond milk
- ½ tsp vanilla extract
- 2 tbsp natural yogurt
- 25g/1oz chia seeds
- Handful of blueberries & almond flakes
- Honey to taste

Method

1 Mix all of the ingredients in a bowl and leave to soak for at least 20 mins until the oats have softened.

2 If the porridge is too dry after this time then add a little water.

3 Divide the mixture between 2 bowls and top each with the blueberries, flaked almonds and honey to taste - or any other combination of fruit and nuts you would prefer.

CHEF'S NOTE

Oats are a great choice for breakfast as they provide slow, sustaining energy. This will help to prevent feelings of fatigue that plague many of us at this life-stage.

LUNCHES
& LIGHT
MEALS

MEXICAN BROTH

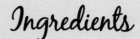 **Ingredients**

- 675g/1½lbs boneless skinless chicken breasts
- 1 tbsp olive oil
- 6 spring onions/scallions, finely sliced
- 2 cloves of garlic, minced
- 2lt/3pts chicken stock
- 2 large tomatoes, seeded and diced

- ½ tsp ground cumin
- ½ tsp ground coriander/cilantro
- A large handful of coriander/cilantro, chopped
- 3 tbsp fresh lime juice
- 3 medium avocados, peeled, cored and diced

Method

1 In a large saucepan heat 1 tbsp olive oil over medium heat. Once hot, add the onions and sauté until tender, about 2 minutes, adding garlic during last 30 seconds.

2 Add the chicken stock, tomatoes, cumin, coriander and season with salt and pepper before adding the chicken breasts.

3 Bring the mixture to a boil over medium-high heat, then reduce heat to medium, cover with a lid and allow to cook, stirring occasionally, until the chicken has cooked through - around 10 - 15 minutes.

4 Reduce the heat to low, remove the chicken from pan and let rest on a cutting board for 5 minutes, then shred the chicken and return to the soup. Stir in the coriander and lime juice.

5 Add the avocados to soup just before serving.

CHEF'S NOTE
This broth retains the aromatic warmth, freshness and zing of Mexican food but without the heat. Chillies are one food that is known to exacerbate hot flushes, so best avoided where possible.

AROMATIC TOFU SALAD

Ingredients

For the salad:
- 4 eggs
- 1 cup cherry tomatoes, halved
- 500g/1lb2oz Chinese greens, chopped into 1-inch chunks
- 1 medium cauliflower, cubed
- 250g/9oz beansprouts

- 175g/6oz Silken Tofu, cubed
- 1 tbsp sesame oil
- ½ cucumber, sliced

For the dressing:
- 125g/4oz crunchy peanut butter
- Juice of 2 limes

- 1 clove garlic
- 2 tsp Asian fish sauce
- 1 tbsp soy sauce

To garnish:
- Crushed peanuts
- Coriander/cilantro

Method

1 Begin by frying the tofu in the sesame oil on a medium heat, for 15 minutes or until golden on all sides.

2 Whilst the tofu is frying carefully lower the eggs into boiling water and boil for 6 minutes until nearly hard boiled. Remove from the hot water and place in bowl of cold water. Once cool peel and cut each in half.

3 Boil or steam the cauliflower for 3-4 minutes to soften slightly, then remove from the water and allow to cool whilst preparing the other ingredients.

4 To prepare the sauce, place all the ingredients in a blender and blitz until you have a well combined, fairly smooth sauce. Season with extra salt and lime juice to taste

5 Add the tofu and cauliflower to the rest of the salad ingredients (except the eggs) and pour over the sauce and mix everything thoroughly.

6 Top with the halved eggs, coriander and crushed peanuts.

CHEF'S NOTE

Tofu is a great addition to your cooking repertoire. Asian countries that eat high quantities of soy products, such as tofu, have been found to suffer less from the symptoms of menopause.

MACKEREL AND BEETROOT SALAD

Ingredients

- 1 smoked mackerel fillet
- 50g/1oz green beans
- 100g/3½oz cooked beetroot

- 25g/1oz baby spinach
- 40g/1¾oz feta cheese, crumbled

Method

1 Simmer the green beans in water for 4–5 minutes.

2 Drain and rinse under cold running water until cool.

3 Flake the mackerel and toss with the beans, the beetroot and spinach in a small bowl.

4 Top with the cheese and serve.

CHEF'S NOTE
Mackerel is bursting with "good fats" which boost brain, body and skin, especially from mid-life onwards.

CHICKEN TIKKA SALAD

Ingredients

- 100g/3½oz ready-prepared, cooked chicken tikka, sliced
- 50g/1¾oz iceberg lettuce, shredded
- 50g/1¾oz cucumber, thinly sliced
- 2 spring onions/scallions, thinly sliced
- 1 tbsp ready-made tzatziki

Method

1 Combine the chicken, cucumber and spring onions in a bowl.

2 Spread the lettuce over a plate and top with the other ingredients.

3 Drizzle the tzatziki on top.

4 Serve immediately or keep in the fridge for a few hours.

CHEF'S NOTE

A decrease in oestrogen levels during menopause has been linked to a loss of muscle mass; this is why it's important to eat a diet high in quality protein, such as the chicken in this salad.

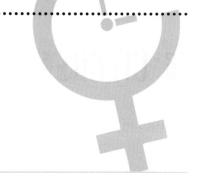

PRAWN AND CAULIFLOWER SALAD

Ingredients

- 100g/3½oz cauliflower florets
- 1 tsp olive oil
- 100g/3½oz cooked peeled prawns
- 1 tomato (100g/3½oz), roughly chopped
- ¼ onion (25g/1oz), finely chopped
- ½ tsp olive oil
- 6 cherry tomatoes, halved
- ½ tsp smoked paprika

Method

1 Preheat the oven to 200C/180C Fan/Gas 6. Pulse the cauliflower in a food processer for 30 seconds, or until finely chopped (it should have the same texture as couscous).

2 Mix in the oil and season to taste. Spread the cauliflower onto a baking tray and bake for 15 minutes.

3 Whilst the cauliflower is cooking, mix all of the remaining ingredients together.

4 Fork the prawn mix through the cauliflower and serve either hot or cold.

CHEF'S NOTE
Foods from the cabbage family, such as cauliflower, are a good choice for women going through menopause because they contain calcium, magnesium and folic acid.

CITRUS SALMON

Ingredients

- 250g/9oz organic salmon fillet, skinned
- 2 tbsp rock salt
- 75ml/3fl oz fresh orange juice
- 1 tbsp lime zest

- 150ml/5fl oz lime juice (about 5 limes)
- 30 coriander/cilantro, finely chopped
- 1 fennel bulb, finely sliced
- 110g/4oz baby salad leaves

Method

1 Lightly sprinkle the salmon fillet with rock salt. Transfer to the fridge and leave for 20 minutes.

2 Remove the salmon from the fridge, carefully wash off all the salt and pat it dry.

3 In a small bowl, mix the orange juice, lime zest and juice together. Add the coriander at the last minute and toss to combine.

4 Slice the salmon at an angle - each piece needs to be about 2-3mm thick. Lay four slices evenly in a straight line onto each serving plate.

5 Spoon all but two tablespoons of the dressing over the salmon. Set aside for about 30 minutes.

6 For the salad, soak the sliced fennel in iced water for 2-3 minutes, before removing and draining. Mix with the salad leaves and the reserved two tablespoons of the ceviche dressing.

7 Place the fennel salad on top of the salmon and serve.

CHEF'S NOTE

Salmon is an excellent source of Vitamin D, a fat-soluble vitamin that helps us make our sex hormones and boost testosterone levels. It's also important for bone health and immunity.

CHILLED TOMATO SOUP

Ingredients

- 1kg/2½lb ripe plum tomatoes washed and halved
- 3 tbsp olive oil
- 3 whole garlic cloves, unpeeled

- A large handful of basil leaves
- 1 garlic clove
- 1 tbsp of pine nuts
- 2 tbsp of olive oil

Method

1 Preheat the oven to 180C/375F/Gas 4

2 Place the tomatoes cut side up in a baking tray, add the whole garlic cloves. Season well with salt and pepper and drizzle over the olive oil. Roast for about 45 minutes, or until the tomatoes are lightly browned and beginning to ooze juice. Remove the tray from the oven and leave to cool for a few moments.

3 Pick out the roasted garlic cloves and squeeze the soft flesh out of the skin onto a place. Place a sieve over a bowl and rub the tomatoes through it to extract the juice and flesh. Rub the roasted garlic pulp through the sieve as well, along with any oily juices from the pan.

4 Place the bowl in the fridge and chill for at least four hours.

5 Chop together the basil, garlic and pine nuts, until you have a fine-grained pulp. Stir into the olive oil.

6 Serve the soup in chilled bowls drizzled with a generous tablespoon of the pesto.

CHEF'S NOTE
Tomatoes complement your bodies oestrogen-progesterone balance which can help control menopause symptoms.

NIÇOISE SALAD

Ingredients

- 900g/2lb tuna fillet
- 1 tbsp cracked black peppercorns
- 2 tbsp light olive oil
- 1 yellow bell pepper
- ½ tbsp vegetable oil
- 2 plum tomatoes
- 175g/6 oz green beans, cooked

- 20 olives
- 2 tbsp virgin olive oil
- 2 tbsp parsley, chopped
- 10 new potatoes, boiled and halved

For the dressing:
- ½ tsp salt
- 1½ tbsp Dijon mustard

- 4 tsp lemon juice
- 1 garlic clove, crushed
- 5 drops Tabasco sauce
- 4 anchovy fillets
- 120ml/4fl oz light olive oil
- 1 egg, yolk only

Method

1 Cut the tuna into 4 equal steaks. Sprinkle each with salt and black pepper. Coat lightly in oil, and refrigerate until ready to cook.

2 Rub the yellow pepper with a little vegetable oil, and grill or roast until the skin is well blistered. Allow to cool, and then peel off the charred skin, remove the seeds, slice into 8 pieces, and place in a bowl. Cut the tomatoes into 6 wedges each.

3 Combine all of the vegetables, season lightly with salt and pepper, and toss with the olive oil, and parsley. Leave to come to room temperature.

4 To make the dressing, combine all the dressing ingredients in a blender, and pulse until smooth and emulsified.

5 To cook the tuna, heat a large grill pan over high heat until almost smoking. Add the fish, and sear for 1-3 minutes on each side.

6 To serve, divide the vegetables among the plates, and place a tuna steak in the centre of each. Surround with a generous drizzle of the dressing, and serve immediately.

CHEF'S NOTE

When oestrogen levels drop during menopause, a woman's risk of developing cardiovascular disease increases. Counter this by eating foods high in omega-3s.

CHICKEN SATAY

Ingredients

- 1 iceberg lettuce
- 1 cooked boneless, skinless chicken breast (about 100g/3½oz)
- ⅓ cucumber
- 1 carrot, peeled and cut into fine matchsticks

- ½ red bell pepper, finely sliced
- 5 radishes, trimmed and sliced
- 15g/½oz fresh coriander/cilantro
- 1 long red chilli, finely chopped
- 3 spring onions/scalions sliced
- Lime wedges, for squeezing

For the satay sauce:
- 3 tbsp crunchy peanut butter
- 1 tbsp chilli sauce
- 2 tsp dark soy sauce
- 2 tsp fresh lime juice

Method

1 To make the satay sauce, put the peanut butter in a small bowl and stir in 2 tablespoons of just-boiled water. Mix in the chilli sauce, soy sauce and lime juice. Transfer to a shallow serving dish and place in the centre of a large board or platter.

2 Trim the bottom of the lettuce and carefully separate 8 large leaves.

3 Cut the chicken breasts into thin slices and place on the board or platter with the satay sauce. Arrange the lettuce leaves, cucumber, carrot, pepper, radishes and coriander in separate piles beside the chicken. Put the chilli and spring onions in separate small dishes on the board.

4 To assemble the wraps, place a selection of the vegetables into the lettuce leaves. Add a couple of chicken slices and then top with the satay sauce, spring onions and chillies to taste. Garnish with the fresh coriander and add a squeeze of lime before wrapping the rest of the leaf around the filling. Serve immediately.

CHEF'S NOTE

Peanuts are strictly speaking not a nut at all but a type of legume. They are high in phytoestrogens and a good support to the body throughout menopause.

VEGETABLE QUINOA SALAD

Ingredients

- 125g/4oz quartered button mushrooms
- 175g/6oz cooked quinoa
- 125g/4oz red bell peppers
- 125g/4oz yellow bell peppers
- 125g/4oz pickled red cabbage
- 125g/4oz sun dried tomatoes
- 125g/4oz grilled Brussels sprouts
- 1 sweet potato
- 60ml/2fl oz olive oil

Method

1 Preheat your oven to 190C/375F/Gas5

2 Using large baking pan, drizzle olive oil and salt and pepper over the mushrooms, peppers and Brussels sprouts.

3 Pierce the sweet potato and bake in the oven with the vegetables for 30 mins or until soft.

4 Build your bowl by layering the mushrooms, peppers, cabbage, sun dried tomatoes, quinoa and Brussels sprouts on top of the sliced baked sweet potato.

CHEF'S NOTE

Quinoa is high in protein and full of B vitamins, which are great for keeping you full and increasing energy levels.

PARSNIP SOUP

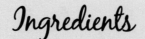

Ingredients

- 1 tsp olive oil
- A pinch of cumin seeds
- A pinch of coriander/cilantro seeds
- A pinch of turmeric
- A pinch of chilli flakes

- A pinch of ground cinnamon
- A pinch of paprika
- ½ red onion, finely chopped
- 1 large parsnip, peeled and chopped
- 200ml/7fl oz vegetable stock

Method

1 Heat the oil in a saucepan over a medium heat and add all of the spices. Add the onion and parsnip and cook for around 3 minutes then add the vegetable stock.

2 Turn down the heat and cook for a further 8-10 minutes or until the parsnip is soft.

3 Leave the soup chunky or blitz in a blender until smooth and serve in a large bowl.

CHEF'S NOTE
Parsnips are high in fibre, potassium, vitamin C and one serving contains a quarter of your recommended daily dose of folate.

PRAWN NOODLES

Ingredients

- 400g/14oz pack cooked prawns
- 300g/11oz pack cooked thin brown rice noodles
- 300g/11oz pack cooked beansprouts

- 3 carrots, thinly sliced
- 1 bunch spring onions / scallions, sliced lengthways
- A bunch mint and coriander/ cilantro, leaves chopped

For the dressing:
- 5 tbsp rice wine vinegar
- 1 tsp caster sugar (optional)
- 1 red chilli, chopped
- 1 stick lemongrass, sliced
- 3 tbsp soy sauce

Method

1 To make the salad put all the vegetables and prawns in a large bowl and mix everything together, so that the seafood and noodles are combined.

2 Then make the dressing by mixing all the ingredients and toss this through the salad before serving.

CHEF'S NOTE
Brown rice noodles mean that this salad will be healthier and satisfying than the more common white rice version, helping to stabilise your blood sugar levels.

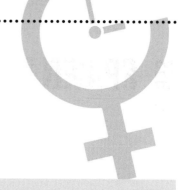

SALMON RICE SALAD

Ingredients

- 200g/7oz brown basmati rice
- 200g/7oz frozen soya beans, defrosted
- 2 salmon fillets
- 1 cucumber, diced
- A small bunch spring onion, sliced

- A small bunch coriander/cilantro, roughly chopped
- Zest and juice 1 lime
- 4 tsp light soy sauce

Method

1 Cook the rice following pack instructions and 3 mins before it's done, add the soya beans. Drain and cool under cold running water.

2 Meanwhile, put the salmon on a plate, then microwave on High for 3 mins or until cooked through. Allow to cool slightly, remove the skin with a fork, then flake.

3 Gently fold the cucumber, spring onions, coriander and salmon into the rice and beans. In a separate bowl, mix the lime zest and juice and soy, then pour over the rice before serving.

CHEF'S NOTE

This dish is packed full of healthy fats, protein and omega 3 from the salmon. The brown rice and fish will help stabilize your blood sugar levels, keeping you full for longer.

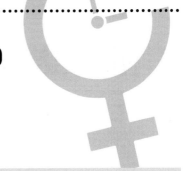

SPICED CHICKPEA WRAP

Ingredients

- 1 400g/14oz can chickpeas
- 1 tsp olive oil
- 1 tsp ground cumin
- 1 tsp smoked paprika
- 1 avocado, stoned, peeled and chopped
- Juice of 1 lime

- Small bunch of coriander/cilantro, chopped
- 4 soft corn or wholemeal tortillas
- ½ small iceberg lettuce, shredded
- 75g/3oz pot natural yoghurt
- 250g/9oz jar roasted red bell peppers, chopped

Method

1 Heat your oven to 200C /400F/Gas 6.

2 Drain the chickpeas and put in a large bowl. Add the olive oil, cumin and paprika.

3 Stir the chickpeas well to coat, then spread them onto a large baking tray and roast for 20-25 mins or until starting to go crisp – give the tray a shake halfway through cooking to ensure they roast evenly. Remove from the oven and season to taste.

4 Toss the chopped avocados with the lime juice and chopped coriander, then set aside until serving. Warm the tortillas following pack instructions, then pile in the avocado, lettuce, yoghurt, peppers and toasted chickpeas at the table.

CHEF'S NOTE

Chickpeas are full of phytoestrogens which stimulate the liver to produce sex-hormone-binding globulin (SHBG) which controls the circulating levels of oestrogen and testosterone in the blood, and also regulates hormone balance.

TUNA AND CANNELLINI BEAN SALAD

Ingredients

- 1 carrot, peeled and coarsely grated
- 1 red bell pepper, deseeded and sliced
- 100g/3½oz pack of sugar snap peas, finely sliced

- 410g/14oz can of cannellini beans
- 125g/4oz of salad leaves
- 3 tbsp vinaigrette
- 200g/7oz can of tuna in brine, drained

Method

1 Mix the carrot, pepper, sugar snap peas and beans together in a large bowl.

2 Gently toss in the salad leaves and half of the vinaigrette, then flake the tuna over.

3 Drizzle with more vinaigrette when you serve.

CHEF'S NOTE

Eating fish and legumes such as cannellini beans daily have been shown by studies to delay menopause by over three years, on average!

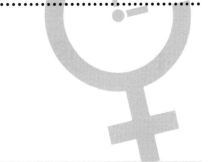

GREEK-STYLE PENNE PASTA

Ingredients

- 85g/3oz wholemeal penne
- ½ lemon, finely grated zest and juice
- ¼ red onion, finely chopped
- ½ tbsp olive oil, ideally extra virgin
- ¼ cucumber, peeled and cubed

- 100g/3½oz cherry tomatoes, quartered
- 15g/½oz fresh basil, roughly chopped
- 60g/2¼oz feta, crumbled
- A handful of pitted black olives

Method

1 Cook the pasta in a saucepan of boiling, salted water as per the packet instructions.

2 Whisk together the lemon zest and juice, red onion, oil and a generous amount of pepper.

3 Drain the pasta in a colander and run it under a cold tap until cooled.

4 Stir the dressing, cucumber, tomatoes, basil, feta and olives into the pasta and serve.

CHEF'S NOTE

Complex carbohydrates, such as wholemeal pasta, help to support the body's adrenal glands, which alongside the fat cells are now the primary source of oestrogen production in the body.

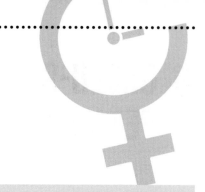

FATTOUSH

Ingredients

- Juice of a lemon
- 1 tbsp olive oil
- ½ Cos lettuce, chopped
- A tomato, chopped into chunks
- ½ small pack flat-leaf parsley, chopped
- 1/4 cucumber, chopped into chunks
- 1 sliced spring onion/scallion
- 1 wholemeal pitta bread
- 1-2 tsp ground sumac

Method

1 Pour the lemon juice into a large bowl and whisk while you slowly add the oil. When all the oil has been added and the mixture starts to thicken, season.

2 Add the lettuce, tomatoes, parsley, cucumber and spring onions, and stir well to coat the salad in the dressing.

3 Put the pitta bread in the toaster until crisp and golden, then chop into chunks.

4 Scatter the toasted pitta pieces over the salad and sprinkle over the sumac. Serve straight away.

CHEF'S NOTE
The wholemeal pitta is a complex carbohydrate which will keep you full and with stabilised blood sugar levels, which will help prevent sugar crashes and cravings.

BLOOD-ORANGE SALAD

Ingredients

For the dressing
- 6 tbsp blood-orange juice (roughly the juice of 1 or 2 blood oranges)
- 1 tbsp pomegranate molasses
- 6 tbsp extra-virgin olive oil
- 2 tsp runny honey

For the salad
- 5 blood oranges
- 1 large fennel bulb
- 125g/4½oz watercress
- About 30 black olives
- 2 balls of good-quality mozzarella
- Extra-virgin olive oil for drizzling

Method

1 Whisk the dressing ingredients with salt and pepper. Taste for seasoning and adjust if necessary.

2 Slice the bottom and top off each orange so they sit flat. Using a sharp knife, cut off the rind and pith in strips, slicing from top to bottom and working your way around each orange. Slice the flesh horizontally, removing any seeds.

3 Quarter the fennel and remove the coarser outer leaves. Trim off the fronds from the top and keep them for the salad. Remove the core from each quarter and then cut very finely (wafer-like is best) preferably using a mandolin.

4 Carefully toss the fennel, watercress, olives and dressing. Carefully drain the mozzarella and, just before serving, tear into pieces. Put on top of the salad. Drizzle with the olive oil and grind on some black pepper.

CHEF'S NOTE

A 2017 study published in the journal of The North American Menopause Society (NAMS) found that the phytoestrogens found in fennel help manage postmenopausal symptoms and pose no adverse effects.

TOFU NOODLE SOUP

Ingredients

- 175g/6oz Silken tofu cut into 1-inch chunks
- 1 vegetable stock cube
- 60ml/1fl oz teriyaki sauce
- 1 tbsp vegetable oil

- 140g/4½oz chestnut mushroom, sliced
- ½ bunch spring onions/scallions, thinly sliced
- 140g/4½oz wholemeal udon noodles
- 200g/7oz bag spinach

Method

1 In a large pan, dissolve the stock cube in 1 litre of water and stir in the teriyaki sauce.

2 While the soup base comes to the boil, heat the oil in a frying pan and cook the mushrooms over a high heat, for 2-3 mins, until they turn golden. Add the spring onions and cook for 1 min more, then set aside.

3 Once the soup base has come to the boil, add the noodles and cook for 4 mins. Add the spinach and tofu and cook for 1 min more until just wilted. Stir in the mushrooms, spring onions and some seasoning, and serve.

CHEF'S NOTE
Tofu contains isoflavone, which breaks down in the body to phytoestrogen; eating this may help ward off menopausal symptoms.

TROUT OPEN SANDWICH

Ingredients

- 2 slices of wholemeal or granary bread
- 1 lemon, halved
- A few dill sprigs, plus extra to serve
- 1 small red onion, ½ sliced, the rest finely chopped
- 2 skinless, boneless wild trout fillets
- 1 small avocado

Method

1 Bring a small pan of water to the boil and add a good squeeze of lemon, a few dill sprigs and the sliced onion. Add the fish and leave to poach for 8-10 mins or until it flakes easily. Lift from the pan and flake into small pieces.

2 Scoop the avocado into a bowl and roughly mash with a generous squeeze of lemon.

3 Top the bread with the avocado, scatter over half the chopped onion, then top with salmon, more onions and some snipped dill. Squeeze over some lemon to serve.

CHEF'S NOTE

Having an open sandwich with only one slice of bread can help you get all the benefits of complex carbohydrates but help to reduce the sluggish felling of excess carb consumption.

LENTIL AND SPINACH SOUP

Ingredients

- 55g/2oz butter
- ½ onion, finely sliced
- 1 garlic clove, crushed
- 1 large tomato, chopped
- 100g/3½oz Puy lentils

- 150ml/¼pt hot chicken stock (vegetarians can substitute vegetable stock)
- 100g/3½oz spinach leaves, washed
- 1 tbsp fresh parsley, chopped
- 1 tbsp basil leaves, chopped

Method

1 Heat the butter in a saucepan and gently fry the onion for 5 mins, until soft but not coloured.

2 Add the garlic and fry for 1 min more.

3 Add the chopped tomato, lentils and chicken stock and bring to the boil. Reduce the heat and simmer for 12-15 minutes, or until the lentils are tender. Allow to cool slightly.

4 Pour the soup into a blender, add the spinach and herbs and blend until smooth. Season, to taste and serve.

CHEF'S NOTE

Puy lentils are rich in energising iron, as well as containing B vitamins to help regulate the nervous system and balance hormone levels.

MAIN MEALS

VEGETARIAN CHILLI

Ingredients

- 2 tbsp extra virgin olive oil
- 5 stalks celery, finely diced
- 2 cloves garlic, minced
- 1½ tsp ground cinnamon
- 4 tsp ground cumin
- 1½ tsp smoked paprika

- 2 green bell peppers, finely diced
- 2 courgettes/zucchinis, diced
- 225g/8oz button mushrooms
- 1½ tbsp tomato puree
- 1 425g/15oz tin of chopped tomatoes

- 750ml/1¼pt of water
- 120ml/4floz coconut milk
- 600g/1lb5oz soy meat, crumbled
- 250g/9oz walnuts, minced
- 1tbsp unsweetened cocoa powder

Method

1 Heat the oil in a large pot over medium heat. Add the celery and cook for 4 minutes. Add in the garlic, cinnamon, cumin and paprika and stir until fragrant, about another 2 minutes.

2 Add the peppers, courgettes and mushrooms and cook for 5 minutes.

3 Add the tomato puree, tomatoes, water, coconut milk, soy meat, walnuts and cocoa powder. Reduce the heat to medium-low and simmer for about 20-25 minutes until thick and the vegetables are soft.

4 Season with salt and pepper, to taste.

CHEF'S NOTE
Using soy substitutes for meat, in this case minced meat, is a great way of upping your intake of phytoestrogens and reducing your red meat intake.

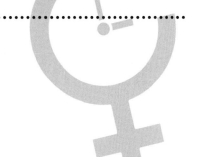

CASHEW CHICKEN STIR-FRY

Ingredients

- 3 boneless chicken thighs
- 2 tbsp coconut oil
- 125g/4oz raw cashews
- ½ medium green bell pepper
- ½ tsp ground ginger
- 1 tbsp rice wine vinegar
- 1 tbsp garlic, minced

- 1 tbsp sesame oil
- 1 tbsp sesame seeds
- 1 tbsp spring onions/scallions
- ¼ medium white onion
- 300g/11oz pack cooked thin brown rice noodles

Method

1 Heat a pan over low heat and toast the cashews for 8 minutes or until they start to lightly brown and become fragrant. Remove and set aside.

2 Dice the chicken thighs into 1-inch chunks. Cut the onion and pepper into equally large chunks.

3 Increase the heat to high and add the coconut oil to the pan.

4 Once the oil is up to temperature, add in the chicken thighs and allow them to cook through (about 5 minutes).

5 Once the chicken is fully cooked, add in the pepper, onions, garlic, and seasonings (ginger, salt, pepper). Allow to cook on high for 2-3 minutes.

6 Add the rice wine vinegar, noodles and cashews. Cook on high and allow the liquid to reduce down until it is a sticky consistency,

7 Serve in a bowl, top with sesame seeds and drizzle with sesame oil.

CHEF'S NOTE
Cashew nuts have a high magnesium content which can stave off insomnia, anxiety, depression and mood swings - as well as boost bone health.

MAURITIAN FISH STEW

Ingredients

- 3 cloves garlic, finely chopped
- 3 cm piece of ginger, finely chopped
- 2 tomatoes
- 1 onion, finely chopped
- 1 tbsp coconut oil, melted
- 1 tbsp garam masala
- 1 tbsp ground cumin

- 1 tbsp turmeric
- 450ml/15floz full fat coconut milk
- ½ tsp salt
- Juice of 1 lime
- 1/2 bunch coriander/cilantro, roughly chopped
- 275g/10oz cod or other white fish chopped into large chunks

Method

1 Put the garlic, ginger, chilli and tomatoes in blender and blitz until smooth.

2 Fry the onion in oil for 2 minutes until translucent, stirring regularly

3 Sprinkle in the spices and fry for 30 seconds. Add in the blitzed ingredients and fry for 3 minutes

4 Add in the coconut oil and salt and raise the heat to bring to a boil.

5 Add in the fish and bring to a simmer. Cook for 3 minutes or until just cooked through.

6 Stir in the lime juice and most of the coriander reserving some to garnish.

CHEF'S NOTE
Coconut oil contains medium chain triglycerides (MCTs), a "good" type of fat that goes straight to the liver to be quickly metabolised into ketone bodies to provide instant energy.

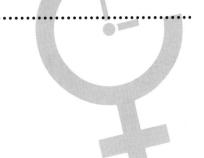

BEEF FILLET WITH ROASTED SHALLOTS

Ingredients

- 12 shallots
- 2 tbsp olive oil, plus extra for brushing
- 1 sprig of fresh thyme
- 1kg/2¼lb beef fillet
- 2 tbsp grated fresh horseradish

- 200ml/7fl oz crème fraîche/sour cream
- 1 tsp white wine vinegar
- 1 sprig of fresh rosemary
- Zest of 1 orange

Method

1 Preheat the oven to 180°C/350°F/gas 4. Toss the unpeeled shallots in the olive oil, season with sea salt and black pepper, and then place them in a shallow baking dish with the thyme sprig. Cover tightly with foil and bake in the oven for 45 mins or until soft.

2 Meanwhile, preheat a heavy griddle pan that's large enough to hold the beef comfortably.

3 Remove all the fat and any sinew from the steak, season well, and brush with olive oil. Place on the hot griddle and sear and brown all over – about 2-3 mins. Take out of the pan and place on a plate to cool for about 30 mins.

4 Mix the horseradish into the crème fraîche. Season it well with salt, pepper and the vinegar.

5 Finely chop the rosemary and finely grate the zest of the orange.

6 Thinly slice the beef with a sharp carving knife and lay 3 slices on each plate. Peel some of the warm shallots, tear them in half and lay a piece on top of each piece of beef. Spoon a little horseradish crème fraîche on top and sprinkle the plates with the rosemary and orange zest before serving.

CHEF'S NOTE

Red meat is higher in saturated fat than poultry or fish, but contains high levels of iron, meaning that it's good to eat once or twice a week for optimal energy levels.

SERVES 6

LAMB AND ANCHOVY BRAISE

Ingredients

- 300g/11oz diced lamb shoulder
- 6 tbsp olive oil
- 4 garlic cloves, crushed
- 1 sprig fresh rosemary
- 2 bay leaves
- 568ml/16fl oz dry white wine

- ½ lemon, juice only
- 1 onion, sliced
- 1 celery stalk, sliced
- 8 anchovy fillets in oil
- 85g/3oz capers

Method

1 Place the lamb pieces into a large bowl and add three tablespoons of the olive oil, the garlic, rosemary, bay leaves, white wine and lemon juice. Stir until well combined, then cover and marinate in the fridge overnight.

2 Preheat the oven to 170C/325F/Gas 3.

3 Remove the lamb pieces from the marinade (but keep the marinade) and pat dry with kitchen paper.

4 Heat the remaining olive oil in a large pan over a medium heat. Add the lamb pieces to the hot oil and fry for 4-5 minutes or until golden brown all over. Transfer to an ovenproof casserole dish.

5 Pour the reserved marinade into the hot frying pan and warm through, then pour it into the casserole with the lamb. Add the onion and celery to the casserole and cook in the oven for 45 minutes, or until the lamb is tender. Add the anchovies and capers and cook for another 15 minutes.

CHEF'S NOTE
Like beef, lamb is full of iron, and the anchovies in this dish are full of omega-3 fatty acids which have impressive anti-inflammatory properties.

MEDITERRANEAN FISH STEW

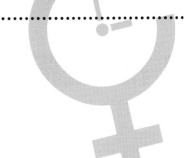

Ingredients

- A handful flat-leaf parsley leaves, chopped
- A garlic clove, finely chopped
- Zest and juice 1 lemon
- 2 tbsp olive oil
- 1 small onion, finely sliced
- 1 tsp paprika

- 400g/14fl oz tin of chopped tomatoes
- 1 fish stock cube
- 100g/3½oz mixed seafood, fresh or frozen
- 250g/9oz white skinless fish fillets such as cod or haddock, cut into very large chunks

Method

1 In a small bowl, mix the parsley with half the garlic and lemon zest, then set aside. Heat 2 tbsp oil in a large sauté pan.

2 Throw in the onion, cover the pan, and sweat for about 5 mins until the onion has softened. Add the remaining oil, garlic and spices, then cook for 2 mins more.

3 Pour over the lemon juice and sizzle for a moment. Add the tomatoes and crumble in the stock. Season with a little salt, then cover the pan. Simmer everything for 15-20 mins.

4 Stir through the seafood and nestle the fish chunks into the top of the stew.

5 Reduce the heat and recover the pan, then cook for about 8 mins, stirring very gently once or twice. When the fish is just cooked through, remove from the heat, scatter with the parsley mix and serve.

CHEF'S NOTE

Parsley is often used as a mere garnish, but as well as adding colour and flavour it is full of phytoestrogens, making it a good addition to many meals.

RED LENTIL CURRY

Ingredients

- 1 tbsp coconut oil
- 2 onions, finely chopped
- 250g/9oz chopped vegetables of your choice
- 2 garlic cloves, crushed
- 20g/¾oz ginger, finely grated
- 2 tsp garam masala
- 400g/14oz tin chopped tomatoes

- 600ml/20fl oz chicken stock
- 100g/3½oz dried red split lentils, rinsed and drained
- 2 bay leaves

To serve:
- 150g/5½oz natural yoghurt
- 1 tbsp fresh coriander/cilantro, roughly chopped

Method

1 Place the coconut oil in a large saucepan over a medium heat. Cook the onions for 5 minutes, stirring regularly, until softened and very lightly browned.

2 Cut your vegetables into bite size pieces and add to the pan. Cook for 2 minutes, turning occasionally. Stir in the garlic, ginger and garam masala and cook for a few seconds, stirring constantly.

3 Tip the tomatoes into the pan and add the chicken stock, lentils and bay leaves. Bring to the boil, then cover loosely with a lid and simmer gently for 35 minutes, or until the vegetables are tender and the lentils have completely broken down, stirring occasionally.

4 Remove the lid for the last 10 minutes of cooking time, stirring regularly so the lentils don't stick.

5 Season the curry to taste. Serve topped with yoghurt and sprinkled with coriander

CHEF'S NOTE
Lentils are an adaptable and tasty pulse that are a complex carbohydrate brimming with phytoestrogens, leaving you healthy and satisfied.

MACKEREL PARCELS

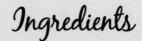

Ingredients

- 375g/13oz mixed red and yellow cherry tomatoes
- 320g/11½oz fine green beans, trimmed
- 2 garlic cloves, finely chopped
- 2 tbsp lemon juice
- 8 red mackerel fillets, approximately

100g/3½oz each
- 1 lemon, finely grated rind only
- 2 tsp baby capers, drained
- 2 spring onions/scallions, finely sliced
- 1 tsp olive oil

Method

1 Preheat the oven to 200C/400F/Gas 6.

2 Put the tomatoes in an ovenproof dish with the beans, garlic, lemon juice and drizzle over the oil. Season with salt and freshly ground black pepper and mix well. Bake for 10 minutes, or until the tomatoes and beans are tender.

3 Meanwhile, tear off 4 large sheets of foil and line with non-stick baking paper. Place 2 fish fillets on each piece of baking paper, then scatter over the lemon rind, capers and spring onions, season with salt and freshly ground black pepper. Fold over the paper-lined foil and scrunch the edges together to seal. Place the parcels on a large baking tray.

4 Place the fish parcels next to the vegetables in the oven and bake for a further 8-10 minutes, or until the flesh flakes easily when pressed in the centre with a knife.

5 Spoon the vegetables on to four serving plates and top each with two fish fillets and serve.

CHEF'S NOTE
Alongside the benefits of oily fish, this dish is made with capers; these contain a progesterone compound called kaempferol, meaning that they will help to balance your hormone levels.

BLACK BEAN AND NUT BURGERS

Ingredients

- 50g/2oz pine nuts
- 425g/15oz can black beans drained and rinsed
- 1 small red onion, finely chopped
- 2 tbsp sundried tomato puree
- 85g/3¼oz ground almonds
- 1 tbsp fresh thyme leaves
- 1 beaten egg
- Sunflower oil, for frying

Method

1 Place a frying pan over a medium heat and lightly toast the pine nuts for 2-3 mins or until golden. Remove from pan and set to one side.

2 Put the black beans into a large bowl and mash well with a potato masher or fork. Add the pine nuts, onion, tomato puree, half of the ground almonds, the thyme and egg. Season to taste, then gently mix together until the ingredients are thoroughly combined.

3 With slightly wet hands, shape the mixture into 4 burgers. Cover and chill in the fridge for at least 30 mins.

4 To cook the burgers: heat a thin layer of sunflower oil in a large frying pan and fry for 3-4 mins each side until golden. Drain on kitchen paper, before serving.

CHEF'S NOTE
Black beans are one of the best foods that you can eat to alleviate menopausal symptoms, as they're high in fibre, magnesium, zinc and antioxidants.

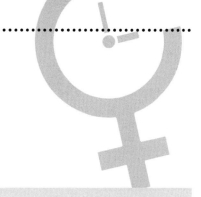

KEDGEREE

Ingredients

- 150g/5oz brown rice
- 1 medium salmon fillet
- 2 eggs
- 1 tbsp vegetable oil
- 1 onion, finely chopped
- 50g/2oz curly kale, stalks removed, rough-
- ly chopped
- 1 garlic clove, crushed
- 1 tbsp curry powder
- 1 tsp turmeric
- Zest and juice ½ lemon

Method

1 Cook the rice following pack instructions. Meanwhile, season the salmon and steam over a pan of simmering water for 8 mins or until just cooked.

2 Keep the pan of water on the heat, add the eggs and boil for 6 mins, then run under cold water.

3 Heat the oil in a large frying pan or wok, add the onion and cook for 5 mins.

4 Throw in the kale and cook, stirring, for 5 mins. Add the garlic, curry powder, turmeric and rice, season and stir until heated through.

5 Peel and quarter the eggs. Flake the salmon and gently fold through the rice, then divide between plates and top with the eggs.

6 Sprinkle over the lemon zest and squeeze over a little juice before serving.

CHEF'S NOTE

Kale is a wonderful ingredient to add to your dishes as it contains as much calcium as a cup of milk, helping to ensure good bone health.

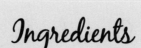

SOLE AND SOYA BEAN MASH

Ingredients

- 2 small bunches cherry tomatoes, on the vine
- 1 tbsp olive oil
- 2 sole fillets
- Zest and juice of 1 lemon

- 240g/8½oz pack frozen soya beans
- 1 garlic clove
- 1 small bunch of basil, leaves and stalks separated
- 100ml/3½floz fish stock

Method

1 Heat your oven to 200C/400F/gas 6. Put the tomatoes onto a baking tray, rub with a little oil and some seasoning, roast for 5 mins until the skins are starting to split.

2 Add the fish to the tray, top with most of the lemon zest and some more seasoning, and then drizzle with a little more oil. Roast for 8-10 mins until the fish flakes easily.

3 Meanwhile, cook the beans in a pan of boiling water for 3 mins until just tender.

4 Drain, tip into a food processor with the rest of the oil, garlic, basil stalks, lemon juice and stock, then pulse to a thick, slightly rough purée. Season to taste.

5 Divide the tomatoes and mash between two plates, top with the sole, then scatter with basil leaves and the remaining lemon zest to serve.

CHEF'S NOTE
An exciting take on fish and mushy peas, this dish will provide all the benefits of phytoestrogens found in soya.

LAMB MEATBALL TAGINE

Ingredients

- 1 small onion, finely chopped
- 2 tbsp olive oil
- 25g/1 oz ground almonds
- 250g/9 oz pack lean lamb mince
- ½ tsp ground cinnamon
- 3 eggs
- 2 garlic cloves, sliced
- 1 courgette/zucchini, thickly sliced
- 400g/14oz cans chopped tomatoes
- 1 tsp honey
- ½-1 tsp ras el hanout spice mix
- A small bunch of coriander/cilantro, mostly chopped
- 400g/14oz can chickpeas, rinsed and drained

Method

1 Fry the onion in 1 tbsp oil until soft, then allow to cool. Mix with the almonds, mince, cinnamon, 1 egg, ½ tsp salt and lots of pepper, then shape into about 12 meatballs with wet hands.

2 Fry in the remaining oil in a shallow pan for about 8 mins, moving them round until evenly browned. Lift out and set aside.

3 Add the garlic to the oil left in the pan and fry until softened. Add the courgette, fry for 1-2 mins, then tip in the tomatoes, honey, ras el hanout, three-quarters of the coriander, seasoning and a couple of tbsp water. Stir and cook until soft and pulpy.

4 Stir in the chickpeas and add the meatballs. Make 2 hollows in the sauce, then break in the remaining eggs.

5 Cover and cook for 4-8 mins over a low heat until the eggs are set. Scatter with coriander and serve straight from the pan.

CHEF'S NOTE
Chickpeas contain high levels of protein and fibre; they work together to slow digestion, which helps promote fullness. In addition, protein may increase levels of appetite-reducing hormones in the body

CHEESY PESTO CHICKEN

Ingredients

- 2 boned, skinless chicken breasts
- 2 slices prosciutto
- 100g/3½oz crème fraiche/sour cream
- 1 ½ tbsp pesto
- 25g grated parmesan
- 1 tbsp pine nuts

Method

1 Heat oven to 200C/400F/gas 6. Season the chicken all over, then wrap each fillet in a slice of ham. Put into a large baking dish.

2 Dot the crème fraîche between the fillets and over the exposed ends of the meat.

3 Dot the pesto around the chicken and scatter with the cheese.

4 Bake the chicken for 15-20 mins, adding the pine nuts halfway through, until the crème fraîche has made a sauce and the cheese and ham are turning golden

CHEF'S NOTE
Like other tree nuts, pine nuts are high in beneficial monounsaturated fats, magnesium and vitamin E, which work together to protect the heart.

MOROCCAN CHICKEN

Ingredients

- 600g/1lb 5oz chicken thigh pieces, cut into bite-size cubes
- 1–2 level tbsp harissa paste
- 400g/14oz tin chopped tomatoes with herbs
- 2 x 400g/14oz tins chickpeas, drained
- 12 dried apricots
- A small bunch (about 30g/1oz) fresh coriander/cilantro, roughly chopped

Method

1 Preheat the oven to 180C/350F/Gas4

2 Put the chicken in a medium, ovenproof casserole dish or tagine and coat evenly with the harissa paste.

3 Pour in the tomatoes and 300ml/10floz of water. Bring to the boil over a medium heat and stir well.

4 Cover tightly with kitchen foil if using a casserole dish or place the lid on a tagine and bake for 1 hour.

5 Stir in the chickpeas and apricots and bake for 30–45 minutes, or until the chicken is cooked through.

6 Stir in the coriander and serve.

CHEF'S NOTE

Dried fruit has something of a bad reputation, due to increased levels of sugar compared to fresh fruit. However, apricots contain higher levels of phytoestrogens, making them a good occasional choice.

CHICKEN CURRY

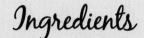

Ingredients

- 2 onions, finely chopped
- 6 chicken thighs, boned
- 2 garlic cloves, crushed
- 20g/¾oz ginger, finely grated
- 2 tsp garam masala
- 400g/14oz chopped tomatoes

- 600ml/20floz chicken stock, made with 1 chicken stock cube
- 100g/3½oz dried red split lentils, rinsed and drained
- 2 bay leaves
- 200g/7oz wholegrain rice

To serve:
- 150g/5½oz fat-free natural yoghurt
- 1 tbsp fresh coriander/cilantro, roughly chopped

Method

1 Spray a wide-based saucepan or sauté pan with oil and place over a medium heat. Cook the onions for 5 minutes, stirring regularly, until softened and very lightly browned.

2 Cut the chicken thighs in half and add to the pan. Cook for 2 minutes, turning occasionally. Stir in the garlic, ginger, garam masala and chilli powder and cook for a few seconds, stirring constantly.

3 Tip the tomatoes into the pan and add the chicken stock, lentils and bay leaves. Bring to the boil, then cover loosely with a lid and simmer gently for 35 minutes, or until the chicken is tender and the lentils have completely broken down, stirring occasionally. Remove the lid for the last 10 minutes of cooking time, stirring regularly so the lentils don't stick.

4 About 25 minutes before the curry is ready, cook the rice in plenty of boiling water until tender, then drain well.

5 Season the curry to taste. Serve with the rice, topped with yoghurt and sprinkled with coriander.

CHEF'S NOTE

Some of the ingredients found in garam masala such as pepper, cloves, cinnamon and cardamom are known to lower bad cholesterol levels, which often creep up during middle-age.

CURRIED EGG

Ingredients

- 2 large free-range eggs
- 1 tbsp light olive oil
- 2 tsp cumin seeds
- 1 tsp black mustard seeds
- 2 tbsp medium curry powder, plus extra for sprinkling
- 1 tsp garlic granules
- 1 tsp ground ginger

- 400g tin chopped tomatoes
- 400g tin chickpeas, drained and rinsed
- 1 tbsp lemon juice
- 100ml/3½floz boiling water
- 180g/6oz baby leaf spinach
- 2 tbsp fresh coriander/cilantro, chopped, to garnish

Method

1 Bring a small saucepan of water to the boil and cook the eggs for 6–8 minutes, or until done to your liking. When cool enough to handle, shell, halve and set aside.

2 Meanwhile, heat the oil in a wide frying pan over a low heat. Add the cumin, black mustard seeds, curry powder, garlic granules and ground ginger and stir-fry for 1 minute.

3 Add the tomatoes, chickpeas, lemon juice and boiling water and season with salt and pepper.

4 Cook over a high heat for 6–8 minutes, or until reduced and thickened, stirring often. Add the spinach and cook until wilted.

5 Divide the curry between two shallow bowls, top each with two egg halves and sprinkle over some curry powder.

6 Scatter with coriander and serve immediately.

CHEF'S NOTE

As we approach middle-age, it's important to counter the loss of bone-density that menopause brings. Spinach and eggs contain calcium, vitamin D and vitamin K2 which help prevent osteoporosis.

71

SALMON AND LENTILS

Ingredients

- 200g/7oz Puy lentils
- 1 bay leaf
- 200g/7oz fine green beans, chopped
- 25g/1oz flat leaf parsley, chopped
- 2 tbsp Dijon mustard

- 2 tbsp capers, rinsed and chopped
- 2 tbsp olive oil
- 2 lemons, finely sliced
- 4 salmon fillets
- 1 fennel bulb, finely sliced

Method

1 Put the lentils in a saucepan with the bay leaf and enough cold water to cover. Bring to the boil, reduce to a simmer and cook for 30 minutes or until tender. Season to taste with salt and freshly ground black pepper. Add the beans and simmer for a further minute.

2 Drain the lentils and discard the bay leaf. Stir in the parsley, mustard, capers and oil.

3 Preheat the grill to a hot setting.

4 Arrange the lemon slices on a foil-lined grill pan and place the salmon and fennel slices on top. Season the salmon and fennel with salt and freshly ground black pepper.

5 Cook under the grill for about 10 minutes, or until the salmon is cooked through.

6 Place the salmon on top of the lentils and fennel slices and serve.

CHEF'S NOTE

Lentils and salmon are both rich in zinc. Studies have found that those who consume high levels of zinc have a later onset of menopause, compared to those who consume little.

MEDITERRANEAN DRUMSTICK BAKE

Ingredients

- 1½ tbsp olive oil
- 1 tsp dried oregano
- 2 tsp cumin seeds
- 8 chicken drumsticks

- 1 butternut squash, cut into chunks
- 2 green bell peppers, roughly chopped
- 150g mixed olives, roughly chopped

Method

1 Heat oven to 200C/400F/Gas 6. Mix the olive oil, oregano and cumin.

2 Put the chicken drumsticks, peppers and squash in a large roasting tin, toss in the flavoured oil and season.

3 Roast in the oven for 45 mins until tender and golden, then tip the olives into the pan.

4 Give everything a good mix, then return to the oven for 5 mins to warm through before serving.

CHEF'S NOTE

Squash is rich in vitamin A, an essential vitamin for healthy skin, teeth, bones, and soft tissue. It also has a high fibre content, which can help with constipation that may accompany the hormonal changes of menopause.

TURKEY PROTEIN BOWL

Ingredients

- 1 tbsp cold-pressed rapeseed oil
- 2 skinless turkey escallops (about 300g/11oz)
- 1 medium onion, sliced into 12 wedges
- 1 red bell pepper, deseeded and sliced
- 2 garlic cloves, finely chopped
- 100g/3½oz green beans, trimmed and cut in half

- 2 tsp ground cumin
- 2 tsp ground coriander/cilantro
- 100g/3½oz uncooked quinoa
- 75g/3oz frozen sweetcorn
- 75g/3oz kale, thickly shredded

Method

1 Heat the oil in a large, deep frying pan or sauté pan.

2 Season the turkey and fry over a medium-high heat for 2-3 mins each side or until golden. Transfer to a plate.

3 Add the onion and pepper to the pan and cook for 3 mins, stirring, until softened and lightly browned.

4 Tip in the garlic and beans, and stir-fry for 2 mins. Add the spices, then stir in the quinoa and sweetcorn.

5 Pour in 700ml just-boiled water with 1/2 tsp flaked sea salt and bring to the boil.

6 Return the chicken to the pan, reduce the heat to a simmer and cook for 12 mins, stirring regularly and turning the chicken occasionally.

7 Add the kale and cook for a further 3 mins or until the quinoa and turkey are cooked through.

CHEF'S NOTE

Turkey is often only eaten at Christmas time, but has in fact many health benefits. It contains tryptophan which is responsible for producing and boosting serotonin, which often dips during menopause.

GINGER SPICED COD

Ingredients

- 1 tbsp oil
- 1 onion, chopped
- 2 tbsp medium curry powder
- A thumb-sized piece ginger, peeled and finely grated
- 1 cinnamon stick
- 3 garlic cloves, crushed

- 400g/14oz tin of chopped tomatoes
- ½ 400g/14oz tin of chickpeas
- 2 cod fillets (about 125-150g each)
- Zest of 1 lemon, then cut into wedges
- A handful coriander/cilantro, roughly chopped

Method

1 Heat the oil in a large, lidded frying pan. Cook the onion over a high heat for a few mins, then stir in the curry powder, ginger and garlic.

2 Cook for another 1-2 mins until fragrant, then stir in the tomatoes, cinnamon stick, chickpeas and some seasoning.

3 Cook for 8-10 mins until thickened slightly, then top with the cod.

4 Cover and cook for another 5-10 mins until the fish is cooked through.

5 Scatter over the lemon zest and coriander, remove the cinnamon stick then serve with the lemon wedges to squeeze over.

CHEF'S NOTE

In a 2017 study looking at the impact of cinnamon, saffron and ginger on menopause symptoms found that consumption of these spices led to a reduction in menopause symptoms.

PEARL BARLEY AND SQUASH RISOTTO

Ingredients

- 75g/2½oz butter
- 1 onion, finely chopped
- 800g-1kg/1lb 12oz-2lb 4oz butternut squash, peeled, seeds removed, diced
- 2 garlic cloves, finely chopped

- 1 litre/1¾ pint vegetable stock
- 250g/9oz pearl barley, rinsed
- 2 sprigs sage, leaves picked and finely sliced

Method

1 Heat a large saucepan over a medium heat. Add 25g/1oz of the butter. Once melted, add the onion and squash along with a pinch of salt. Gently fry for 10 minutes, or until the onion is translucent and the squash is softening. Add the garlic and continue to cook for 2 minutes.

2 In a separate pan, warm the stock and half of the sage leaves.

3 Add 25g/1oz of the butter to the onion and squash and, once melted, add the pearl barley. Turn up the heat and cook for 2-3 minutes. Turn down the heat to medium and add a ladleful of warm stock. Stir well to mix and, once absorbed, add another ladleful, stirring now and again. Repeat this process until the stock is used up and the pearl barley is tender (about 30 minutes).

4 Once the barley is tender, taste and season to taste with salt and pepper. Add the remaining butter to the pan and stir through.

5 Serve the risotto garnished with the remaining sage.

CHEF'S NOTE
Barley is often underused, but is a delicious and a rich source of fibre, vitamin B1, chromium, phosphorus, magnesium and niacin - as well as lignans, a group of antioxidants linked to a lower risk of cancer and heart disease.

SNACKS, TREATS & SIDE DISHES

WILD RICE SALAD

Ingredients

- 250g/9oz chestnut mushrooms, halved
- 1 onion, finely chopped
- 2 garlic cloves, crushed
- 1 unwaxed lemon, finely grated zest only
- 150g/5½oz mix of brown basmati and wild rice, rinsed
- 375ml/13floz hot vegetable stock
- 1 pomegranate, seeds only
- 5 spring onions/scallions, finely chopped
- 100g/3½oz watercress, roughly chopped

For the lemon and coriander dressing:
- 2 tbsp extra virgin olive oil
- 15g/½oz fresh coriander/cilantro, roughly chopped
- 2 tbsp lemon juice

Method

1 Preheat the oven to 200C/400F/Gas 6.

2 Place the mushrooms, onion, garlic, lemon zest, rice and vegetable stock in a casserole dish or small, deep roasting tin. Cover tightly with kitchen foil or a lid and cook for 1 hour.

3 Meanwhile, to make the lemon and coriander dressing, mix all the ingredients together in a small bowl. Set aside.

4 Stir the dressing, half the pomegranate seeds, half the spring onions and the watercress into the rice. Taste and adjust the seasoning, if needed. Garnish with the remaining pomegranate seeds and spring onions. Serve immediately.

CHEF'S NOTE
Pomegranates contain large amounts of phytoestrogens and antioxidants which can provide cardiovascular protection – about which every menopausal woman should be aware.

BABA GANOUSH

Ingredients

- 3 aubergines/eggplants
- 3 garlic cloves, crushed with a teaspoon of salt
- 1 lemon, juice only

- 2 tbsp tahini
- 3 tbsp olive oil
- Black pepper, to taste
- 1 tbsp flat leaf parsley, chopped

Method

1 Prick the aubergines with a fork, then grill until the skin is charred and blacked and the flesh feels soft when you press it (this will take approximately 15-20 minutes, turning halfway through cooking).

2 In a pestle and mortar, crush the garlic with the lemon juice, tahini, olive oil and pepper.

3 When cool enough to handle, cut the aubergines in half and scoop out the flesh. Mix the soft flesh with the remaining ingredients.

4 Place in a serving dish and finish with a drizzle of olive oil and sprinkle the parsley over the top.

CHEF'S NOTE
Tahini is made from ground sesame, a great source of omega-6. There is some evidence that it may be able to help bind excess hormone metabolites and increase their clearance from the body.

TAPENADE

Ingredients

- 1 garlic clove, crushed
- 1 lemon, juice only
- 3 tbsp capers, chopped
- 6 anchovy fillets, chopped

- 250g/9oz black olives, pitted
- A small bunch fresh parsley, chopped
- 2-4 tbsp extra virgin olive oil

Method

1 Mix all the ingredients together, adding enough olive oil to form a paste.

2 Alternatively, for a smoother texture, add the garlic, lemon juice, capers and anchovy into a food processor and process for about 10 seconds.

3 Add the olives and parsley and enough olive oil to make a paste.

4 Season to taste if necessary.

CHEF'S NOTE
Olives and olive oil are good additions to your diet as they're very high in phytoestrogens, which reduce menopausal symptoms and help protect against osteoporosis.

KALE CRISPS

Ingredients

- 1 tsp garlic granules
- 250g/9oz curly kale, leaves picked from stems, washed and dried
- ¼ tsp sea salt
- 1 tbsp light olive oil

Method

1 Preheat the oven to 140C/275F/Gas 1 and line two large baking trays with baking paper.

2 Mix together the garlic granules and sea salt.

3 Put the kale in a large bowl and massage the oil into the leaves. Toss with the seasoning.

4 Spread the leaves out in a single layer on two large baking trays. Bake for 20 minutes, turning the trays halfway through cooking.

5 Lift the leaves from the baking paper using a spatula. Return the trays to the oven, turn off the heat and leave for 12–15 minutes, or until crisp.

CHEF'S NOTE

Kale is known as a superfood for good reason: it's full of vitamin D and calcium, helping to protect your bones as you enter your next life-stage

STUFFED AVOCADO

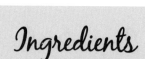

Ingredients

- 2 avocados
- 175g/6oz smoked salmon

- 175ml/6fl oz crème fraiche/sour cream
- 2 tbsp lemon juice (optional)

Method

1 Cut the avocados in half and remove the pit.

2 Place a dollop of crème fraiche in the hollow of the avocado and add the smoked salmon on top.

3 Season to taste with salt, pepper and a squeeze lemon juice before serving.

CHEF'S NOTE
Full of healthy fats and omega-3, this works as a great starter for a dinner party or even a healthy breakfast. It also works well with other fatty fish such as smoked mackerel or trout.

SPICED NUTS

Ingredients

- 1 egg white
- 1 tsp cayenne pepper
- 1 tsp cumin
- ½ tsp salt
- 170g/6 ½oz mixed nuts

Method

1 Heat oven to 150C/130C fan/gas 2.

2 Lightly whisk the egg white, then add the spices and salt. Add the mixed nuts and coat well.

3 Spread out in a single layer on a lightly oiled baking sheet and bake for 12 mins. Cool before eating.

CHEF'S NOTE

As well as being full of healthy fats, nuts are packed with protein. Studies have shown that regular consumption may prevent the loss of lean muscle, aid in weight loss and help regulate mood and sleep.

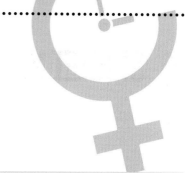

CASHEW NUT BUTTER

Ingredients

- 300g/11oz cashews
- 1 tbsp butter

Method

1 Heat oven to 170C/325G/Gas 3. Spread the cashews on a baking tray and roast for 10 mins. Remove and allow to cool.

2 Put into a food processor and whizz for 12 mins, stopping every so often to scrape the sides down, and finish with the butter to combine.

CHEF'S NOTE

Cashews are full of magnesium which can stave off insomnia, anxiety, depression and mood swings - as well as boost bone health.

SEEDED CRISPBREADS

Ingredients

- 175g/6oz sesame seeds
- 60 g/2½oz sunflower seeds
- 60 g/2½oz grated hard cheese
- 1tbsp ground psyllium husk powder
- 100ml/3½fl oz water
- 2 eggs
- ¼ - 1 tsp salt

Method

1 Preheat the oven to 180C/350F/ Gas 5

2 Mix together all of the ingredients and spread out on parchment paper on a baking sheet. Sprinkle sea salt on top and then bake for 20 mins.

3 Remove and carefully cut the crackers into the desired form

4 Lower the heat to 140C/ 275F/ Gas 1 and cook for another 40 minutes.

5 Remove the crispbreads and make sure they're dry all the way through.

CHEF'S NOTE
Sunflower seeds are rich in zinc, magnesium, potassium and iron. They are also a good source of vitamin E, which may help alleviate hot flushes.

QUINOA SALAD

Ingredients

- 300g/11oz quinoa
- 1 red onion, finely chopped
- 85g/3¼oz raisins or sultanas
- 100g/3½oz feta cheese, crumbled
- 200g/7oz pomegranate seeds

- 85g/3¼oz toasted flaked almonds
- Small pack each of coriander/cilantro, flat leaf parsley and mint, roughly chopped
- Juice of 3 lemons

Method

1 Cook the quinoa following pack instructions – it should be tender but with a little bite.

2 Drain well and spread over a platter or wide, shallow bowl to cool quickly and steam dry.

3 When the quinoa is just about cool stir through all the remaining ingredients with plenty of seasoning.

CHEF'S NOTE

Quinoa contains high levels of quercetin and kaempferol which have anti-inflammatory, anti-viral, anti-cancer and anti-depressant effects.

MEDITERRANEAN BUTTER BEANS

Ingredients

- 540g/1lb 3oz jar large butter beans
- 500g/1lb 2oz tomatoes, peeled and cored
- 1 red chilli
- A bunch of basil
- 1 garlic clove
- 1 tbsp olive oil
- 1 tbsp red wine vinegar

Method

1 Drain and rinse the butter beans and place in a mixing bowl. Chop the tomatoes and add to the beans.

2 Place the chilli, basil (reserving a few small leaves) garlic, olive oil and vinegar in the small bowl of a food processor then whizz until smooth.

3 Add to the tomatoes and beans, season and mix.

4 Serve scattered with a few small leaves.

CHEF'S NOTE

Butter beans are an excellent source of protein, iron and fibre, including a type of fibre that helps lower cholesterol.

SPICED CAULIFLOWER AND CHICKPEAS

Ingredients

- 1 large head of cauliflower, broken into florets
- 2 garlic cloves, crushed
- 2 tsp caraway seeds
- 2 tsp cumin seeds
- 3 tbsp olive oil

- 400g/14oz tin of chickpeas, drained and rinsed
- 100g/3½oz pine nuts
- Small bunch each parsley and dill, leaves torn

Method

1 Heat oven to 200C/400F/Gas 6. Toss the cauliflower, garlic, spices, 2 tbsp oil and some seasoning in a roasting tin, and then roast for 30 mins.

2 Add the chickpeas, pine nuts and remaining oil to the tin, then cook for 10 mins more.

3 To serve, stir in the herbs.

CHEF'S NOTE

This side-dish is jam-packed with phytoestrogens from the cauliflower, chickpeas and pine nuts, making it a perfect choice if you're suffering from symptoms of menopause.

QUINOA STUFFED PEPPERS

Ingredients

- 4 red bell peppers
- 1 courgette/zucchini, quartered length-ways and thinly sliced

- 2 x 250g/9oz packs ready-to-eat quinoa
- 85g/3¼oz feta cheese, finely crumbled
- A handful parsley, roughly chopped

Method

1 Heat oven to 200C/400F/Gas 6. Cut each pepper in half through the stem, and remove the seeds.

2 Put the peppers, cut-side up, on a baking sheet, drizzle with 1 tbsp olive oil and season well. Roast for 15 mins.

3 Meanwhile, heat 1 tsp olive oil in a small frying pan, add the courgette and cook until soft. Remove from the heat, then stir through the quinoa, feta and parsley. Season with pepper.

4 Divide the quinoa mixture between the pepper halves, then return to the oven for 5 mins to heat through.

CHEF'S NOTE
Fibre is essential during menopause as it helps maintain blood sugar levels and ensures a healthy hormone balance by binding to old oestrogens in the gut, ensuring they're eliminated and not re-absorbed into the bloodstream.

ASIAN SEED MIX

Ingredients

- 1 egg white
- 2 tsp Chinese five spice powder
- ½ tsp salt
- 85g/3¼oz each sunflower and pumpkin seeds

Method

1 Heat oven to 150C/300F/Gas 2.

2 Lightly whisk egg white, then add Chinese five-spice and salt.

3 Add sunflower and pumpkin seeds, and coat well.

4 Spread out in a single layer on a lightly oiled baking sheet and bake for 12 mins. Cool before eating.

CHEF'S NOTE
Seeds are a great source of protein and healthy fats, making them a perfect snack before, during and after menopause.

HOUMOUS

Ingredients

- 2 x 400g/14oz cans of chickpeas in water, drained
- 2 fat garlic cloves, roughly chopped
- 3 tbsp Greek yoghurt
- 3 tbsp tahini paste
- 3 tbsp extra-virgin olive oil, plus extra for serving
- Zest and juice of 2 lemons
- 20g pack coriander/cilantro

Method

1 Put everything but the coriander into a food processor, then whizz to a fairly smooth mix.

2 Scrape down the sides of the processor if you need to.

3 Season the houmous generously, then add the coriander and pulse until roughly chopped.

4 Spoon into a serving bowl, drizzle with olive oil, then serve.

CHEF'S NOTE
Coriander can decrease the frequency hot flashes in perimenopausal women and it is also useful for promoting cognitive function.

CASHEW AND BROCCOLI STIR-FRY

Ingredients

- 100g/3½oz broccoli, cut into florets
- 55g/2oz cashew nuts, toasted
- 2 tbsp soy sauce
- 1 tbsp sesame oil

Method

1 Bring a saucepan of salted water to the boil.

2 Add the broccoli and cook for 5-6 minutes, or until tender.

3 To serve, drain the broccoli and put it into a serving dish.

4 Scatter the cashew nuts over the broccoli, then dress it with the soy sauce and sesame oil.

CHEF'S NOTE
Broccoli is a fantastic source of phytoestrogens as well as vitamins K and C, folate (folic acid) and potassium.

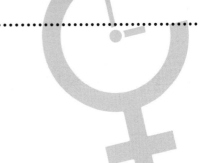

CHOCOLATE NUT CLUSTERS

Ingredients

- 250g/9oz chocolate chips
- 60ml/2fl oz coconut oil

- 450g/1lb salted mixed nuts

Method

1 Line a rimmed baking sheet with parchment paper or a silicone baking mat.

2 In a microwave-safe bowl, combine the chocolate chips and coconut oil and microwave until the chocolate is melted. Use a rubber spatula to mix until smooth. Allow to cool slightly.

3 Add the nuts to the bowl with the melted chocolate. Mix until all the nuts are well coated.

4 Drop large spoonfuls of the mixture onto the prepared baking sheet. Be sure to space them out enough that they do not run together.

5 Refrigerate until solid. Store leftovers in an airtight container in the refrigerator for up to 3 weeks.

CHEF'S NOTE

All nuts (including coconuts) are good sources of mono and polyunsaturated fatty acids (healthy fats) and help balance insulin levels which helps prevent weight gain.

FRUIT AND NUT BARS

 Ingredients

- 400g/14oz soft pitted dates
- 300g/10½oz cashew nut pieces
- 4 tbsp cacao or cocoa powder
- 1 tbsp almond butter
- 1 tbsp coconut oil
- 1 tbsp vanilla essence
- Water

Method

1 Grease and line a 20x20cm/8x8in baking tray.

2 Put all the ingredients into a food processor and blend until the cashew nuts become tiny pieces.

3 Remove the lid and add 1 tablespoon of water and blend again. If the mixture is not already sticking together, add another spoon of water and blend again. Repeat until the mixture starts to stick together.

4 Using a spoon or spatula, transfer the mixture into the lined tray. Press the mixture into the tin and put in the fridge to set for at least an hour.

5 Remove from the fridge and slice into 12 bars or smaller chunks.

CHEF'S NOTE

Dates are high in fibre as well as several types of antioxidants that may help prevent the development of certain chronic illnesses, such as heart disease, cancer, Alzheimer's and diabetes.

POACHED ORANGES

Ingredients

- 2 x 150g/5½oz pots natural yoghurt
- 3 oranges
- A pinch of ground cinnamon
- 2 star anise
- ¼ tsp vanilla extract
- 10g/¼oz toasted flaked almonds

Method

1 Cut one of the oranges in half and squeeze all the juice – you should end up with 4-5 tbsp. Peel the remaining oranges and cut into thin slices.

2 Pour the juice into a small saucepan and stir in the cinnamon, star anise and vanilla extract

3 Place over a medium heat and simmer for 1-2 minutes, stirring occasionally. Add the orange slices and warm through gently.

4 Place the warm spiced oranges and juice into 2 bowls and spoon the yoghurt and scatter the nuts on top.

CHEF'S NOTE

Decreasing oestrogen levels leads to lower levels of collagen, leaving skin wrinkled, dry, and at greater risk of sun damage. Therefore, it's important to maintain vitamin C levels to protect skin tissue and promote wound-healing.

ETON MESS

Ingredients

- 4 meringue nests
- 300g/10½oz strawberries, halved
- 300ml/10floz plain yoghurt

Method

1 Place the meringue nests into a freezer bag and scrunch them up until broken into pieces.

2 Mash half of the strawberries with the back of a fork until almost smooth.

3 Layer the ingredients into serving glasses. Start with some strawberries, along with a spoonful of their juices. Mix half of the crushed meringues through the yoghurt and add some of this to the glass.

4 Top with a bit more fruit and some of the crushed meringues. Repeat until all the ingredients are used up and the glasses are full. Serve immediately

CHEF'S NOTE
Ensuring you have adequate levels of calcium as you approach menopause is essential for maintaining bone health. Dairy products, such as yoghurt are one of the best sources.